READER'S PASSAGES
to accompany

BADER
READING AND
LANGUAGE INVENTORY

Fourth Edition

Lois A. Bader
Michigan State University

Merrill
Prentice Hall

Upper Saddle River, New Jersey
Columbus, Ohio

ACKNOWLEDGMENTS

Permission to reprint from the following publishers is greatly appreciated:

Addison-Wesley Publishing Company. Adapted from *Just Awful,* ©1971 by Alma Marshak Whitney, by permission
of Addison-Wesley Publishing Company, Inc.

Prentice Hall: *History of a Free People,* 10th Revised Ed., by Henry W. Bragdon and Samuel P. McCutchen. Copyright ©1981 Prentice-Hall, Inc.: *Background for Tomorrow: An American History* by Bertha Davis, Dorothy S. Arnof, and Charlotte Croon Davis, Upper Saddle River: Prentice-Hall, Inc., 1969: SERIES: *Prentice Hall Reading 1980,* Carl B. Smith and Ronald Wardhaugh, Senior Authors, Copyright ©1980 Prentice-Hall, Inc., PAST TO PRESENT: A WORLD HISTORY by Sydney H. Zebel and Sidney Schwartz, Copyright ©1960 Prentice Hall, Inc.

The Putnam Publishing Group: Reprinted by permission of Coward, McCann & Geoghegan, Inc. from *The Aquanuts,* copyright ©1971 by Arthur Schaffert.

The H. W. Wilson Company: "Waukewa's Eagle" by James Buckham, published by D. Appleton-Century Company, Inc. in *St. Nicholas Magazine,* copyright ©1900 and 1928, and the version of "Waukewa's Eagle" by Katherine Williams Watson in *Once Upon a Time.* The H. W. Wilson Company, copyright ©1942.

Q
428
B 134r

Vice President and Publisher: Jeffery W. Johnston
Editor: Linda Ashe Montgomery
Production Editor: Mary M. Irvin
Design Coordinator: Diane C. Lorenzo
Cover Designer: Rod Harris
Cover Photo: Photo 20/20
Production Coordination and Text Design: Carlisle Publisher Services
Production Manager: Pamela D. Bennett
Director of Marketing: Kevin Flanagan
Marketing Manager: Krista Groshong
Marketing Coordinator: Barbara Koontz

This book was set in Times Roman by Carlisle Communications, Ltd., and was printed and bound by Courier Kendallville, Inc. The cover was printed by Phoenix Color Corp.

Earlier edition © 1983 by Lois Bader

Prentice-Hall International (UK) Limited, *London*
Prentice-Hall of Australia Pty. Limited, *Sydney*
Prentice-Hall Canada, Inc., *Toronto*
Prentice-Hall Hispanoamericana, S.A., *Mexico*
Prentice-Hall of India Private Limited, *New Delhi*
Prentice-Hall of Japan, Inc., *Tokyo*
Prentice-Hall Singapore Pte. Ltd.
Editora Prentice-Hall do Brasil, Ltda., *Rio de Janeiro*

10 9 8 7 6 5 4 3 2
ISBN 0-13-092964-6

Contents

TIP THE CAT

Tip is a cat.

She likes to eat fish.

She is a fat cat.

Tip eats fish and sleeps.

She likes to sit on my lap.

She is a good pet.

ON THE BUS

We are going home.

Stop and go.

Stop and go.

The bus is so slow.

Look at that man.

He has a bike.

He can go fast.

THE DOG SHOW

I went to a dog show.

I saw big dogs.

I saw little dogs.

I saw dogs with long hair.

I saw dogs with short hair.

There were dogs everywhere.

LEE'S FRIENDLY MEAL

Lee was a little blue fish.

Some of his friends were very big fish.

Lee's big friends lived far away.

But he saw them every day.

Every day they would swim by to see Lee.

When they came, Lee liked to eat.

Lee ate the tiny animals off the big fish.

This made the big fish happy.

And Lee got his lunch.

TURTLES AT HOME

Turtles are always at home.

If they visit the sea, they are at home.

If they go to the high hills, they are at home.

If they go far away, they have a home.

Turtles carry their homes with them.

Their shell is their house.

Turtles stay in their shells.

That is why they are always at home.

A SLIPPERY SIDEWALK

It was a cold day.

A man fell on the ice.

He was not hurt.

"Put salt on the ice," said Bill.

"Salt will melt the ice."

"Salt can kill the grass," said Pat.

"Put sand on the ice."

"I will try to find some sand," said Bill.

"But it is better to kill some grass than

    have a bad fall."

PAT AND THE KITTEN

Pat saw a kitten. It was on the side of the street. It was sitting under a blue car.

"Come here, little kitten," Pat said. The kitten looked up at Pat. It had big yellow eyes. Pat took her from under the car. She saw that her leg was hurt.

"I will take care of you," Pat said. She put her hand on the kitten's soft, black fur. "You can come home with me."

The kitten gave a happy *meow*.

TONY AND THE FLOWER SHOP

Tony lived in a big city. He ran a flower shop. Tony loved his flowers, for the flowers did not make any noise. Tony loved peace and quiet.

The city where Tony lived was noisy. The buses, trucks, and cars were very noisy. He did not like the noise of the city.

Without the quiet Tony found in the flower shop, he would have moved from the city. The flower shop was his only reason for staying in the city.

GIVE ME ROOM

I saw an old man get on the bus. He walked very slowly.
He used a cane. I looked at the cane with surprise. The man
had a bike horn on it. I told him I had never seen a cane with
a horn. "Have you ever been to the city market?" he asked. I
said that I had. "Then you know it is crowded," he said.
"People did not give me room. Now I honk my horn and they
move."

THE SONG OF LITTLE FROG

Little Frog lived by a lake. He did not have many things. He only had a house to live in, a bed to sleep in, and an old pot to cook with. He had one old book that he read again and again. Still Little Frog was happy.

Near his house there were many pretty flowers. The birds sang all day. Little Frog liked to look at the pretty flowers. He liked to hear the birds sing. Little Frog wanted to sing like the birds. But when he tried to sing, all that came out was a *ribbit ribbit*.

SAM BUYS A NEWSPAPER

Sam stopped to ask Mrs. Kay if she needed anything from the store. She was very old. Sam liked to help her. She asked him to buy her a newspaper.

The store was closed. Sam walked for a long time to another store. He asked for a newspaper. One was folded and put into his bag.

Sam gave Mrs. Kay the paper. She said, "Oh, Sam, you are so good. I have not seen a paper written in Greek for months!"

Sam was surprised, but he just said, "You're welcome, Mrs. Kay."

LINDA AT THE DINER

Linda has a part-time job in a diner. She works in the morning from six until ten. The diner is busy at breakfast time. Linda works hard, but she likes her job at the diner. She likes talking with people. Many of the same people come in every day.

At night Linda goes to school. She likes night school. She has made new friends in her classes. The teachers are very nice.

Linda wants to learn more about business. She hopes to become a manager of a diner. Then she wants to buy her own diner someday.

JAMES' CUT

It was after lunch when James cut his finger on the playground. He was bleeding and he hurt a little, too.

He went inside to find his teacher. He showed her his cut finger and asked for a Band-Aid. She looked at it and said, "Well, it's not too bad, James. I think we should wash it before we bandage it, don't you?" James did not want it washed because he thought it would sting. But he was afraid to tell Miss Smith. He just acted brave.

When it was washed and bandaged, he thanked Miss Smith. Then he rushed out to the playground to show everyone his shiny new bandage.

TODAY'S EXPLORERS

Astronauts fly far away from the earth. They explore space and the moon. Maybe, in time, they will explore other worlds, too. Deep-sea divers go to the floor of the sea. They explore places just as strange and wonderful as astronauts do.

You may have seen some beautiful fish in the ocean. If you were a diver, you could go far under water. You could stay there long enough to see many unusual creatures. You would find things you never dreamed of.

The only way you could stay underwater for more than a short time is to use special gear. You must use the same kind of gear divers use. A large air tank lets you stay under water for an hour.

Today, explorers go under the sea and far into space.

THE LUCKY WRONG NUMBER

Sue and Bill were eating dinner when the telephone rang. Bill said, "I'll get it." A man asked if the washer could be delivered in the morning.

Bill said, "We did not order a washer."

The man said, "Is this the home of P.J. Johnson?"

"No," Bill said, "but wait; P.J. Johnson is our uncle's name, and we haven't seen him in a long time. What address do you have for him?"

The caller said, "201 Second Street."

Bill and Sue went to the address of P.J. Johnson. He was their uncle. They were happy to see each other. Later Sue said, "Buying that washer was lucky."

Uncle P.J. laughed, "I didn't buy a washer; I bought a TV. We just had a lucky wrong number."

CHECKERS GAME FOR KIM

Kim has an arm that does not work well. Sometimes Kim gets angry with her left arm because it doesn't do what she wants it to and accidents happen. When this happens, Kim gets mad and she calls her arm useless. Kim knows that with lots of exercise her left arm will work better and she will be able to do more things. Kim tries to exercise her arm as much as she can. Exercise is very hard work, but Kim keeps trying.

One way that Kim likes to exercise her arm is to help her dad make things in the workshop. She has fun working with her dad. They have just finished making a special checkers game. The checkers go into holes in the board. This will help Kim. The holes will keep the checkers from being knocked off the board by her arm. She enjoyed helping make the game because she loves to play checkers. Kim likes to work with her dad, and it is good exercise for her arm.

THE RECOVERY

In three small rooms lived a mother and her daughter, who was quite ill. The mother worked every day. She worked hard but could afford little more than rent, food, and clothes. Because of this, the little sick girl would stay quietly in bed at home while her mother was away.

The mother worried about her daughter. If only she had someone to talk to or something to keep her mind busy.

One morning as the mother was leaving for work, she saw a little hurt bird huddled on the window sill. Her daughter insisted that it be brought in so she could care for it.

That evening when the mother returned, the daughter was more talkative than she had been for a while. Every evening after that, she noticed that both the girl and the bird were improved. They seemed to draw strength from each other.

Then one day the mother returned home to find the table set. Tears came to the mother's eyes when the little girl said they must celebrate, for the bird was better.

LAND OF MANY RICHES

In 1869, the American Secretary of State, William Seward, did something that many people thought was foolish. He bought a huge piece of land called Alaska. He bought Alaska for only two cents an acre from a country called Russia. But many people thought the purchase was a waste of money. To them Alaska was just a useless land of rocks, snow, and ice.

However, the following years have proved these people wrong. Some of the riches found in Alaska have made the purchase worthwhile. One of these riches is the trees in Alaska's huge forests. Much of the land in Alaska is covered by forests. The trees are cut and sold to all parts of the world.

The sea around Alaska is full of riches, too. Many fish, such as codfish, herring, crabs, and shrimp, live there. They are caught and sold to the rest of the United States and the world. Alaska has been worth much more than it cost because many riches have been discovered there.

WAUKEWA'S EAGLE

One morning when the boy called Waukewa was hunting along the mountainside, he found a young eagle with a broken wing. It was lying at the base of a cliff. The bird had fallen from a ledge and, being too young to fly, had fluttered down the cliff. It was hurt so severely that it was likely to die. When Waukewa saw it, he was about to drive one of his sharp arrows through its body. But then he saw that the young eagle at his feet was quivering with pain and fright. Waukewa slowly stooped over the panting eagle. The wild eyes of the wounded bird and the keen, dark eyes of the boy met. The boy's eyes grew gentler and softer as he gazed at the bird. Then the struggling of the young eagle stopped. The wild, frightened look passed out of its eyes. And the bird allowed Waukewa to pass his hand gently over its ruffled feathers. The desire to fight, to defend its life, gave way to the charm of the tenderness and pity expressed in the boy's eyes. From that moment, Waukewa and the eagle were friends.

THE NILE VALLEY

The early settlers in the Nile Valley had to root out the jungle and drain the marshes. Once it was cleared, the flood-enriched soil produced good crops. The rich soil caused many tribes to come to settle in the valley. In time some of these tribes learned that more land could be farmed if there was water for the long dry season. They worked hard to build a lake in which to store the water. They dug miles of canals and ditches to distribute the water to the fields.

This was a large task, which required the work of many tribes. Out of common need, the many different tribes had one leader to plan and direct their work. Once the water system was built, the leader supervised its repair and controlled the flow of water into the canals. Through his control of the water, he became a powerful ruler.

NOT IN THE MOOD TO READ

Have you ever heard someone say, "I used to like to read, but now I am not interested in reading"? Carlos used to say that. Then one day he found that he could not read the small print on a medicine bottle. Carlos had his eyes tested, and he was told he needed glasses. The day Carlos put them on, he stopped at a paperback bookstore and bought a sports magazine, a paperback mystery, and a newspaper. Carlos's eyes had never hurt, so he hadn't thought about needing glasses. It seemed good to be reading again. Carlos had forgotten how much he enjoyed reading.

There are many people, both children and adults, who believe they don't feel like reading or doing close work. Their vision is poor, but they do not know that they are having problems with their sight. However, there are others who know they should wear glasses but don't want to wear them. They think glasses may not be attractive. This is not necessarily true. Glasses now have such nice looking frames that some people wear them who don't need them! In fact, lenses in their glasses are just plain window glass.

EARLY TOOLS

Before humans discovered how to obtain and work metals, they made their tools out of wood, bone, and stone. At first they simply used the materials in their natural forms. Then they learned to alter the materials to produce tools to fit the tasks. Wood was split or shaved with sharp rocks and polished on sandstones. Pointed stones were used to bore holes in wood. Fire was also used to shape wood. After a portion of the wood was burnt, the charcoal was scraped away. This process was repeated until the desired shape was achieved.

Bone was broken into many different-sized splinters that were used as gouges, knives, and needles.

For the most part, the wood and bone tools have not survived to this day. But it is still possible to find ancient stone tools.

Stone tools were shaped by two methods. They were struck with rocks or pieces of antler or shaped by applying pressure at points where a flake was likely to break off.

Many people have found arrowheads. Most of these were actually used as spear points. Only a very small stone head would be light enough to use with an arrow and bow.

CONSTELLATIONS

People all over the world have looked at the stars and have seen patterns that reminded them of everyday things. A group of stars that forms such a pattern is a constellation. A constellation lies within a definite region of the sky. By knowing the positions of the constellations, one can locate stars, planets, comets, and other galaxies. There are eighty-eight officially recognized constellations.

Many of the ancient names for certain constellations are still used today, though the things they were named for are no longer a part of our everyday experiences.

Almost anyone who grew up in the Northern Hemisphere can point out the Little Dipper. The Little Dipper is part of the constellation Ursa Minor, which means Little Bear.

Ursa Minor appears to circle the North Star. It is visible all year long. Some groups of stars are only visible during certain seasons of the year.

There are twelve seasonal constellations that are especially important because the sun and the moon always rise within one of their patterns. These are the constellations of the Zodiac.

Constellations are used in ship and airplane navigation. Astronauts use them to help orient spacecraft.

DRIVER'S LICENSES

States vary in their requirements for a driver's license. Some will give a license to persons sixteen years of age, while others will not. Usually the consent of a parent or guardian is needed if an applicant is under eighteen. Generally, people need to fulfill three important requirements to get a driver's license. Drivers have to prove skills in driving a vehicle and knowledge of rules and safety procedures. They also have to be physically capable of safe driving. For example, people who are nearsighted are often issued restricted licenses. This means that they must wear glasses or contact lenses when they drive.

Responsible people drive carefully to avoid hurting others or themselves. Most of us realize that having a driver's license suspended or revoked can be very inconvenient. This is especially true when driving is needed for daily commuting to work.

Some states have a system of points. This means that for every violation the driver has, there are so many points held against him or her. If a driver has too many points in a particular period, the license to drive will be suspended. The system seems helpful since people don't want to lose their driving privileges .

VOLCANOES

Powerful forces within the earth cause volcanoes. Scientists do not fully understand these forces. But they have developed theories on how the forces create volcanoes.

A volcano begins deep in the earth, where it is hot enough to melt rock. The molten rock is mixed with gases and floats up through the solid rock around it. Where the earth's crust is weakest, the liquid rock sometimes channels through it and explodes onto the surface in a volcanic eruption.

The melted rock is magma when it is still within the earth. But once it reaches the earth's surface, it is lava.

The lava flows out of the central channel and smaller side channels in streams or in sheets that overlap each other like waves on a beach.

The main gas released by a volcano is steam. Because the steam contains volcanic dust, it looks like smoke.

When the magma is sticky, rock fragments of various sizes are also thrown off by the explosion. The largest fragments are called bombs.

The material brought to the surface during a volcanic eruption sometimes forms a mountain around the opening of the central channel. A mountain that was formed by a volcano will have a large, bowl-like crater in its center, and it is also called a volcano.

QUESTIONS ABOUT DINOSAURS

Since the first dinosaur fossils were discovered, scientists have been curious about how they lived. One question was, did dinosaurs take care of their young? We know that dinosaurs laid eggs. Ducks lay eggs and they raise their young ducklings. But turtles lay eggs and, when the eggs hatch, the young turtles are on their own. When we think about birds, snakes, alligators, and other creatures that lay eggs, we can see that some care for their young and others do not.

The question about dinosaurs was answered when scientists found dinosaur footprints with the large prints on the outer circle and very small footprints on the inside. This discovery meant that the adult dinosaurs were protecting the young ones. If you have seen reports on elephants, you probably know that this is exactly what the adult elephants do. They form a circle with each elephant in the herd facing outward so they can see lions or other animals approaching them. The tiny young elephants are safe inside the circle.

Scientists continue to ask questions, look for clues and try to interpret what they find. Because dinosaurs were very different from each other in size, eating habits, and other ways, we don't know if all dinosaurs raised their young. Many questions have been answered about dinosaurs, but more questions remain.

THE JOB APPLICATION

Tina wanted a job in an office. A magazine publishing company had some openings, so Tina went to the personnel department. The receptionist gave her an application form and asked her to go into the next room and complete it. The form was only two pages long, but it had several parts. At the top of the first page, Tina had to write her name, address, and social security number. She was glad that she had put her social security card in her wallet. Next Tina was asked about her record of business experience. That part was easy too, except for the box that said, "Reason for separation." Tina was puzzled, but then she realized they were asking why she had lost her other job. She thought she could explain why she left, but Tina didn't know how she could write the reason in such a tiny box.

The last part of the application asked for three references' names, occupations, and addresses. Tina could not remember the addresses of her references. She didn't know whether to leave that part blank or come back later. Then she had a better idea. Tina used the telephone directory to find the correct addresses. Tina decided that before she applied for any more jobs, she would write down the kind of information needed on applications and take it with her.

KON-TIKI

In 1947, six men set out to cross the Pacific Ocean from Peru to Polynesia—4,300 miles of open ocean—on a raft! This was the famous *Kon-Tiki* expedition, led by Thor Heyerdahl, a Norwegian archaeologist.

These men were attempting to prove that the people of Polynesia had originally come from Peru by crossing the ocean on a raft and that they had been led by a man called Kon-Tiki. Since no one would believe that it was possible to make such a voyage, these six decided to show that it was. They built a raft similar to the ancient Peruvian ones. They took no modern equipment except for a small radio. Nothing steered their craft besides the wind and current; yet they succeeded in making the crossing.

Erik Hesselberg, the only licensed sailor on board, was the navigator of the raft, which was named *Kon-Tiki*. He was also an accomplished artist. He brought along a bottle of ink. He sketched a little every day on the raft in order to have a record for his friends and family.

A SHOPPING TRIP

Gene and Kim had been shopping for equipment for their camping trip. For several days they had been going from store to store looking for things they needed. Shopping was taking a lot of time and was very inconvenient. Their neighbor said that he had been shopping by sending for things through a mail-order catalog for years. Gene said that he had heard about mail-order shopping, but he was worried about getting their money back if something was wrong with the purchase. When the neighbor told Gene and Kim that the store offered a refund guarantee, they asked him if they could borrow his catalog.

Kim noticed that people could order merchandise three ways. They could place a telephone order, or mail an order form, or go to the mail-order counter of the store. Since the nearest mail-order store was far away from them, they planned to order by mail.

Gene felt that they had not completely wasted their time by looking through department stores because they could compare the catalog prices with the prices of items they had seen. They were both pleased to find that the measurements of hiking boots were given so that they would be able to tell whether they would fit.

A NEW JOB

Maria was interested in a job in a canning factory. She did not have much work experience, but her brother had a good job in the factory as a supervisor. Maria remembered that he had not had any experience when he started to work there.

At the personnel office, Maria was given an application form to fill out. There was a section that listed several physical problems such as rheumatism, dermatitis, and back trouble. Maria had not heard of some of the conditions, but she decided that if she didn't know what they were, she didn't have a problem with them.

Next, Maria had to check the times she was willing to work: day shift, second shift, or third shift. Because she was taking a class in adult education in the evening, she decided to check day shift and third shift. Maria hoped for the day shift, but she realized that, as a new employee without seniority, she would probably get the third shift.

Finally, Maria filled in the part of the form that asked about apprentice training. She had just finished a vocational training program that had given her some experience, so she was happy to fill in that part.

When Maria returned the completed form, she was told that she would be notified within two weeks about her employment with the company.

MODERN CHEMISTRY

One of the founders of modern chemistry was a wealthy Frenchman, Antoine Lavoisier, who lived in the late eighteenth century. Lavoisier burned different substances in a closed chamber and proved that there was no change in their weight. This showed that the basic elements remained the same even though their appearance was completely altered.

To explain this phenomenon, an English chemist, John Dalton, proposed the atomic theory in 1810. According to Dalton's theory, all matter is composed of minute building blocks, which he called atoms. The atoms of the different elements vary in size and characteristics. Though the elements themselves can and do combine to form new substances, their atoms always remain the same.

Guided by this theory, a Russian scientist, Dmitri Mendelyeev, arranged all of the known elements in a table according to their atomic weights. He showed that the elements fell naturally into certain groups with similar properties. Since many gaps appeared in the table, chemists began to search for the missing elements .

The field of science contains many examples of discoveries being shared by people from different nations. Because lack of communication can be disastrous to the growth of knowledge, most scientists are eager to compare results and learn from each other.

A FAILURE TO COMMUNICATE

When two people speak the same first language, they occasionally misunderstand each other. Imagine the difficulties that interpreters have when they must first understand what the speaker of one language has said and then translate the message into another language.

Translators are challenged when the speaker makes a reference to an event or story character that is not known to listeners from another country. A speaker may refer to someone as a "Cinderella," meaning that a person was once poor and is now wealthy, but if the listeners do not know the story, the meaning is lost.

Translating quickly, while the first person is speaking, is especially difficult. Yet, simultaneous translation is used today in about 85 percent of all international meetings. Not only are translators working with the United Nations, but they are employed for business, scientific, and educational meetings as well.

Computers are being programmed to translate languages. Although computers have great potential for speedy translations, they have some of the same problems that human translators have. In an early attempt to translate English into Russian, a computer translated, "out of sight, out of mind," as "invisible idiot."

In our global society we need to work hard to understand each other and keep a sense of humor.

VOTER DRIVE

Soon after Jim moved to Plainfield, he received a telephone call from a person who asked if he was registered to vote in the coming election. Jim said that he hadn't thought about it. The caller said she was a member of a local organization that was sponsoring a voter drive. She didn't represent any particular political party but only wanted to encourage people to register and to vote.

Since registration terms and procedures differ from one part of the country to another, the people working in the voter drive offered to explain the local procedures and tell people where they could register.

The caller explained that after Jim registered, he would be mailed a sample ballot for each election. The ballot would contain the names of the candidates and the measures to be voted on.

Jim asked some questions and then thanked the caller for giving him information about voter registration.

Frequently people say that they don't bother to vote because one vote is not significant. Jim read that a presidential election, referred to as the Revolution of 1800, resulted in Burr and Jefferson having the same number of votes. Jim appreciated being reminded about voter registration when he recalled that important tie.

IMPRESSIONISTS

Many schools of modern art have arisen, but we have space to describe only a few. The earliest group, the Impressionists, sought to capture on canvas the impression a person gets when he looks at a scene casually. They therefore merely sketched in the main features in bold brush strokes, allowing the observer's mind to fill in the details. Similarly, they did not mix pigments on a palette in the traditional style. Instead, they used dabs of the basic colors that the viewer's eye blends to form the desired shades. Examined at close range, the Impressionists' paintings seem a blotch of colors and forms. But when the viewer steps back, they suddenly seem to come alive.

The Impressionists' work, unlike more conventional paintings, generally appeared rather flat. The founder of the post-Impressionist school, Paul Cezanne, experimented for years to remedy this weakness. He finally succeeded, by distorting the shapes of objects and using thick layers of carefully blended colors, in creating on canvas the illusion of solidity and depth.

While one may prefer a particular school of painting, an attempt should be made to understand several approaches to visual interpretations and expressions. The rewards are several: a fresh perspective, an understanding of others, and an enrichment of the aesthetic senses.

GLOBAL WARFARE

Soon after it reached the White House, news of the attack on Pearl Harbor was broadcast to the American people. Many will never forget hearing newscasters breaking in on symphony concerts, football games, and children's programs to tell of the awful event. The next day the president asked Congress to accept the "state of war" that Japan's "unprovoked and dastardly attack" had thrust upon the United States; Congress accepted the challenge without dissent.

Although a brilliant military feat, the attack on Pearl Harbor eventually proved to be a colossal blunder on the part of the Japanese. To be sure, it cleared the way for an easy conquest of the Philippines and the East Indies by crippling the American naval forces in the Pacific. But the unprovoked attack united the American people as almost nothing else could have done. In their anger they forgot the bitter partisan quarrels over foreign policies and thought only how to best win a war that no one had wanted.

Subsequent analysis of the political and economic policies that contributed to the outbreak of war revealed that the events that culminated in the great war in the Pacific were the result of many factors.

After hostilities ended, both countries worked toward a harmonious relationship.

When World War II ended, representatives from many nations worked through the United Nations to develop mechanisms for avoiding the recurrence of another nightmare of violence, death, and destruction. Yet wars have continued to occur. The fighting in Southeast Asia and in the Middle East has horrified people who hoped never to see more bloodshed. Nations struggle against nations for economic, political, and cultural reasons. Resolution of complex problems are slow; yet they must come. Another global conflict, with or without the nuclear holocaust, must be avoided.

IMPROVEMENT FOR WORKERS

When states first passed laws regulating labor conditions, they ran into a serious difficulty. Employers challenged the laws, claiming that they interfered with a worker's freedom to work on whatever terms he chose. In 1908 a case came before the Supreme Court in which the new progressive point of view on this kind of legislation was first expressed. An Oregon law protecting women workers was called a violation of the due process clause of the Fourteenth Amendment. The lawyer defending the state of Oregon produced pages and pages of evidence to reveal how the health of women would be jeopardized unless they were protected from employers who forced them to endure long hours and paid them a meager wage. The health of women, it was argued, in the long run would affect the welfare of the nation. The Supreme Court declared that the Oregon law was constitutional.

This case was by no means the last time the Fourteenth Amendment was employed in an attempt to block reform legislation. But the decision in favor of Oregon did encourage many states to pass laws protecting labor, and the courts upheld several of them.

During periods of economic stress, pressure is often brought to bear on legislators to repeal laws that protect employees. One argument frequently heard is that by paying wages below the minimum standards, employers can afford to hire more people, thereby decreasing unemployment. Those representing workers are quick to point out that there is no guarantee that employers would expand their hiring and that improving the economy is a better alternative than offering starvation wages. A high standard of living and good working conditions are not easily surrendered.